the very best of Purple Ronnie

To Mel,

Happy Birthday 1997!

Lots of love

from

Stell xxx

Also by Purple Ronnie

Purple Ronnie's Book of Love

☆

Purple Ronnie's Guide to Life

☆

The Smashing World of Purple Ronnie

☆

Purple Ronnie's Star Signs

☆

Purple Ronnie's Love Poems

Published in 1995 by Statics (London) Ltd,
41 Standard Road, London NW10 6HF
Tel: 0181-965-3327

© 1995 Purple Enterprises Ltd

ISBN 1-873922-43-4

Print origination by Diva Graphics

Printed in England by H.P.H. Print Ltd
Unit 3, Royal London Estate, 29 North Acton Road,
London NW10 6PE

Words by: Giles Andreae
and Simon Andreae

Pictures by: Janet Cronin
and Giles Andreae

Contents

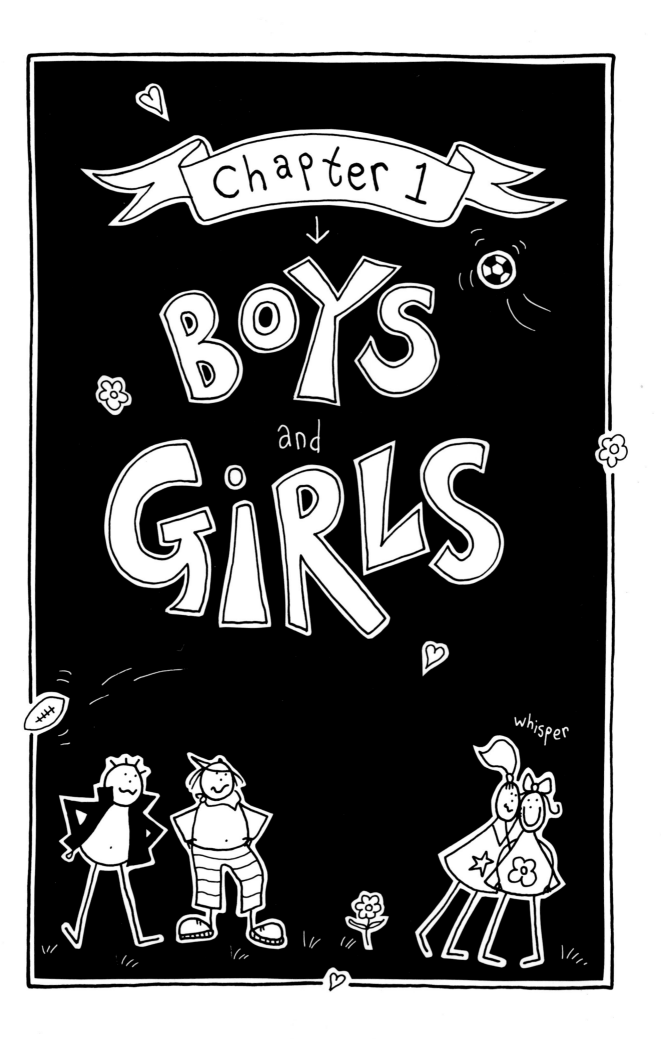

a poem for a

BOYFRIEND

You're a hunky handsome heart-throb
You're a fab and groovy dude
You're a juicy lump of
                    gorgeousness
A scrumptious plate of food
You're a hot and horny lover
And if I had my way
I would smother you in
                    chocolate
And feast on you all day

by
Purple
Ronnie

At first boys think girls are rubbish but when they get older they start to think of them in a different way

As soon as boys begin to dream about hugging and kissing girls all the time horrid things happen to them

Their voices go all wobbly →

Hair grows out of their faces →

They smell and get covered in spots →

But girls just get prettier and prettier

This means that boys have to learn tricks to make girls fancy them. Here are some of the best ones ↓

1. When you talk to girls, don't say too much about how amazing you are but tell them all sorts of things about themselves

actually I'm the complete hero of the school and millions of girls think I'm great but never mind about me you must be the most amazing bunch of smashingness since we all crawled out of the sea

swoon

oooh he's so charming

2. A very good trick is always to tell pretty girls you think they're brainy and tell brainy girls you think they're pretty

I don't care if you are incredibly sexy cos it's your brains that I fancy

at last a boy who really understands me

sucker

proper ← brainbox

3. Always be as mysterious as possible

so what's your name?

it's a long story and crammed full of strange memories from ages ago and miles away and things like that

I just want to wrap him up and take him home

4. When you're with a girl, don't keep telling your mates how you think it's going

5. Don't show off about eating and drinking and making horrid smells. Girls don't like that kind of showing off

6. Quite a good way to make a girl fancy you is to pretend you fancy someone else

How to Be a Boyfriend

Sometimes you've got to be macho
And do lots of things that are tough
But sometimes it's best to be quiet and gentle
And say loads of soppy type stuff

It's good to have hundreds of muscles
And girls always like a nice bum
But you mustn't be hairy or sweaty
or fat
Or have any flab on your tum

♡

Don't ever talk about football
Or make nasty smells in the bed
Or joke about bosoms with mates
in the pub
Or drink till you're out of your head

You've got to be funny and clever
And do loads of things by surprise
Like shouting out loud in the back
of the bus
"My girlfriend's got beautiful eyes!"

You don't need to have too much money
But make sure you've just got enough
To buy loads of presents and chocolates
and flowers
And sexy silk undies and stuff

Say to your girlfriend "you're gorgeous
Your body's a twelve out of ten
You're sexy and beautiful, clever and kind"
Then tell her all over again

The Ways Boys and Girls Think

BOYS

Boys' brains are like great big meat pies with lots of jelly and gristle inside and their heads are made of cement

chewy fat and gristly bits

thick crust ↓

rock hard ↑

This means it is difficult to get new thoughts into a boy's head

let's go to the seaside
why don't we have a romantic walk?
I want to go shopping
who wants to go to the fun fair?
can we go to the disco?

I know let's get pissed and watch football

GIRLS

Girls' brains are more like huge fluffy clouds. Sometimes this means that incredibly complicated thoughts can shoot around in them like lightning...

If Purple and Gordon are friends and Neville fancies Shirlee and Purple loves Maisy but Gordon is Shirlee's best mate then that means Gordon definitely fancies ME!

... sometimes that air and space is the only thing in there

... and sometimes that there are terrible thunderstorms when the only thing to do is run for it

Boys are easier to understand because their brains are wired straight to their privates so they mostly only think of one thing

But girls brains are more complicated and can think about lots of things at the same time

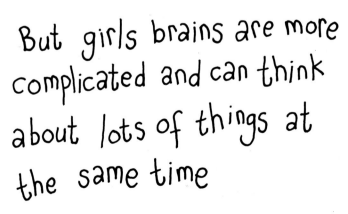

a poem about

Macho Men

Some men think it's cool to bare

A bulging chest with loads of hair

But if you talk to one you'll find

His brains are stuck up his behind

by Purple Ronnie

a poem about floozies

They love to go shopping together
And spend all the money they have
At night they just dance round
their handbags

And laugh about boys in the lav

by Purple Ronnie

The Differences Between Boys and Girls

Girls KISS each other's cheeks

Boys SHAKE each other's hands

Girls LAUGH at jokes

Boys SLAP their thighs

Girls GIVE little creatures warm milk

Boys STAMP on little creatures

When girls are sad they give each other **HUGS**

When boys are sad they **PUNCH** each other's chests

When girls say good bye they **PAT** each other

When boys say good bye they **HIT** each other on the back

GIRLS KISS, LAUGH, HUG, GIVE, AND PAT
BOYS SHAKE, SLAP, STAMP, PUNCH, AND HIT

The reason why boys do these things is that they want girls to think they are <u>hard</u>, and if you poke boys and girls in the chest you will see that boys <u>are</u> harde

But on the inside boys are very soft because when they're not with girls they spend most of their time cuddling each other . . .

CUDDLING MATCHES

At Cuddling Matches all the men dress up in shorts and get into two gangs

There is one man who skips and dances and puts his hands up.
He is the Snuggle Judge who is called the referee

phreep

When he blows his whistle the gangs run towards him and get ready to have a mass Snuggle. They do this by bending over and holding onto each other's pants

squidge

grunt

oof

Someone tries to put a ball into the snuggle but the men are having such a cosy time that they just scrape it out of the way

The players then take it in turns to run around and make each other fall over by hugging their legs

Some of the men in cuddling matches put special shields in their mouths in case people from the other gang try to snog them, which is <u>not</u> in the rules

The differences between Hunks and Weeds

Boyfriends come in 2 styles :-

HUNKS: who are macho and bossy and tell you what to do all the time

AND

WEEDS: who are dreamy and funny and don't even know what to do themselves

Here is how to tell the difference :-

Girls think hunks are tough

Weeds think girls are tough

Hunks make a rumpus

Weeds make a fuss

... more differences

Hunks chew lumps of meat

Weeds cook fancy dishes

Hunks ride motorbikes

Weeds write poems

Hunks think love is rubbish

Weeds think love is an art

a poem about a

HANGOVER

me and my beer

I sometimes wake up in the morning
And try to get out of my bed
But it feels like my tongue
Has been dipped in some dung
And a rhino's charged into my head

zonk

beastie

charge

urg

Plonk   Beer   Plonk

Beer

by Purple Ronnie

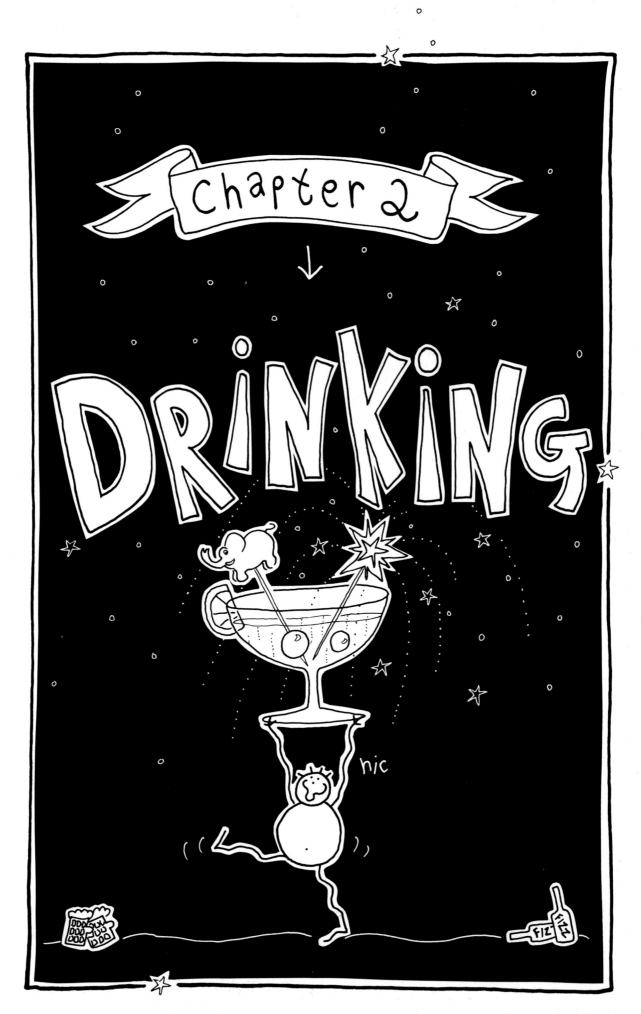

Drinking

Drinking is one of the main things that keeps us alive. If we didn't drink we'd go all dry and crumbly like biscuits and people would have to sweep us up off the floor.

The main drink is water which you can tell by 3 things

1 It's completely see-through

2 Well...um... it's sort of ...quite...kind of... just wet — It doesn't taste of anything

3 ? You don't feel any nicer after you've had some

Because water is so boring lots of people got together and tried millions of experiments to invent other sorts of drinks

Some people took off their shoes and stamped on huge piles of grapes

squish

hic

Some people tried to make tasty recipes with plants and flowers

And some people just squeezed out their mouldy vegetables

whiff

The one thing they all came up with was BOOZE

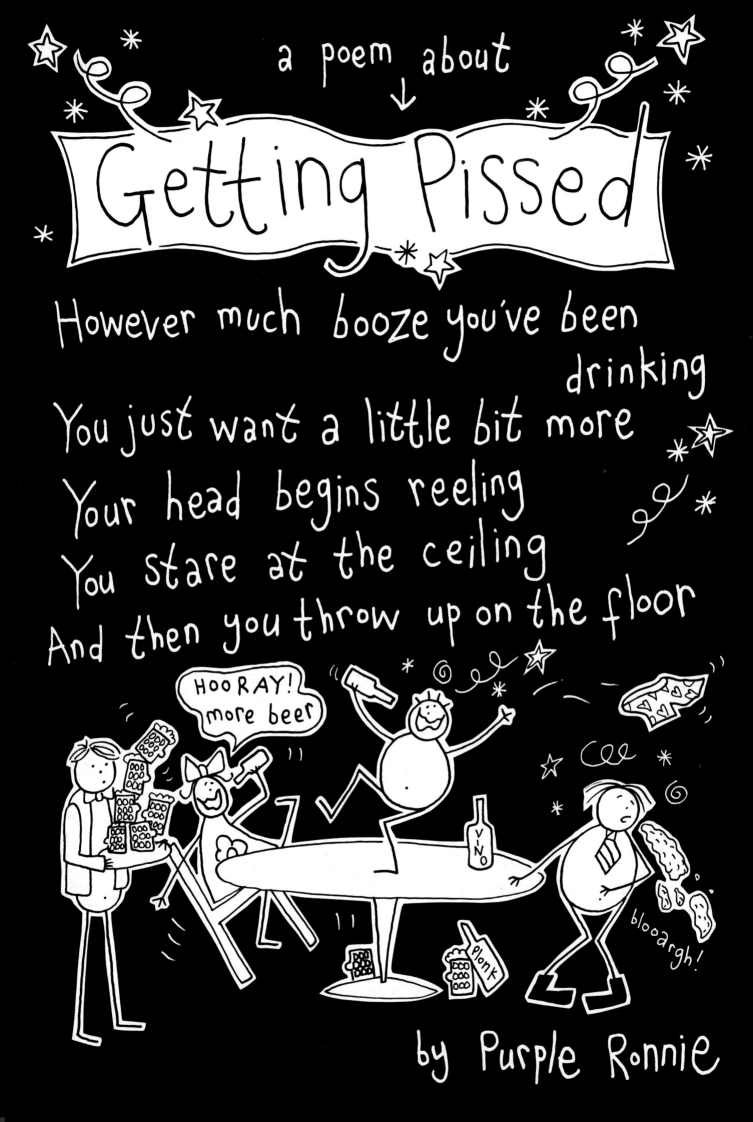

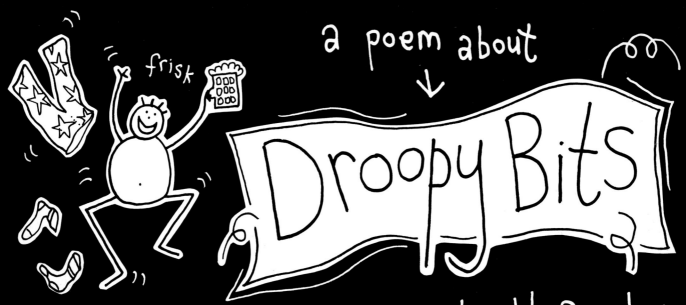

a poem about ↓

Droopy Bits

Drinking makes men get all frisky
And chuck off their clothes in a
heap
They then want to Do It like
crazy
But find that their Thingie's asleep

frisk

please
please
please
please!

not
again!

hic

zzz

by
Purple
Ronnie

Plonk

~ Drinking Chart ~

Drip: only to be used on tiny animals for seeing if they're still alive

Sip: Makes you feel a tiny bit braver. Good for taking before pulling off a plaster

Glass: Makes you feel warm and smiley all over

2 Glasses: Makes you feel like snogging the sauciest people in the room

Jug: Makes you feel like Doing It with anyone in the room

Fishbowl: You start to do silly things and think you're incredibly funny

Bathtub: Your head starts to whistle and you suddenly don't feel like Doing It with anyone at all

Swimming Pool:

a poem about

lager louts

double vindaloo botty burner special

Lager louts love going out with
the lads
In fact it's their favourite trick
To gobble down masses of curry and
beer
And pass out in piles of sick

by Purple Ronnie

a recipe for
Love Pie

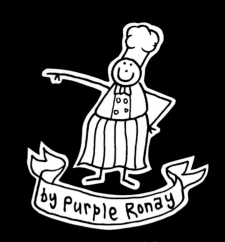

by Purple Ronay

Take a pint of tickle juice
And whisk it till it's thick
Pick a crop of cuddle fruit
And crush them with a stick

Nibble eighteen earlobes
As gently as you can
Then grate a little botty kiss
And put it in the pan

Dip a snog in snuggle sauce
And let it rest a while
Then soak it in hug marinade
and season with a smile

Add a pinch of happy spice
Grown in huggle town
And bake it in the oven
Till it comes out
golden brown

Love

Love comes in all sorts of shapes and sizes and you can use it in all kinds of ways

money love

beer love

me love

rude love

Loving your Mum is not the same as loving beer and sweets and loving your mates is not the same as loving your GIRLIE

matey love

NO SNOGGING

Here are some poems which show the 3 main differences in what WE MEAN BY

↓

LOVE

I have called them the Jammy Bun Poems

Jammy Bun Poem 1

When I think of Jammy buns
I rush off to the shop
And say I want a million please
Then scoff them till I pop

wobble

me about to blow up

Mr Bunman

Jammy Bun Poem 2

Neville is a splendid chap
Oh crikey he's so nice
I'd like to buy a Jammy bun
And offer him a slice

titchy piece of Jammy bun

Jammy Bun Poem 3

My tummy starts to jump around
And then my brain goes swirly
But not because of Jammy buns
But cos I'm with my girlie

whizz

swirl

skip

)) gambol

no buns

I **LOVE** my girlie so much I don't even THINK
of Jammy buns when I'm with her. This is the
kind of **LOVE** that makes you dance and skip
(even if you're a boy) and do all sorts of silly
things - sometimes even ⎪T.

Make sure you give things the right kind
of LOVE or else
you might get in a
frightful muddle and
start DOING IT with
a Jammy bun

I love You
I love You....
I want to have
your babies

Yikes!

?

Hugging

Ever since people were invented they have spent most of their time thinking up all sorts of brainy words so they can talk to each other about incredibly grown-up things and tell each other how amazingly clever they are

24 HOUR Dingle slip job — 20p —

We'll have to scrunge the wibblesnack with a tickling hose and scragglepoop the bottyhiss with a double grundle

hiss

OIL

it's either that or a full dingleslip to the trouser pipe

The problem with words is that they are useless when you want to tell people how you're feeling and talk about what's going on INSIDE YOU

ache   boing

x-ray machine

My Own Little Way

I sometimes get rather embarrassed
And don't always know what to say
When it comes to expressing my feelings
But I try in my own little way

I sort of... well... it's just that... ...well...

shuffle

?

P.R.

THE ONLY LANGUAGE PEOPLE CAN REALLY USE TO SAY IMPORTANT THINGS IS THE LANGUAGE OF HUGGING

hug master →

Hug

A hug is the deepest way there is for one person to say something to another. It is given standing very still with the eyes closed.
You hold each other so tightly that your feelings are squodged together into one ginormous feeling of LOVELINESS

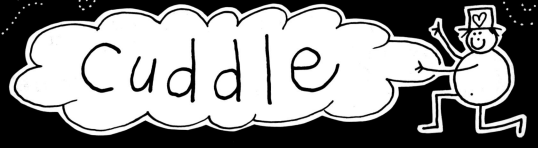

cuddle

A cuddle is shared between 2 people who want to say the same thing to each other.
You can cuddle while:

SITTING   or   LYING DOWN

jiggle   jiggle

You hold each other more loosely than in a hug, and jiggle around until your feelings are nicely shaken about and mixed together

You always come out of a cuddle SMILING

Snuggle

A snuggle is used mainly for warmth and comfort and can <u>only</u> be had lying down

Snuggling is done under warm blankets....

or

.....in little hidey holes

It is wet-nosed and gentle and good at keeping monsters away

Yikes!

← scared monster

Huggle

Yippee!

A huggle is only used by people who are bubbling over with happiness. You can huggle while dancing, jumping or skipping down the street. Huggles can say ANYTHING YOU LIKE. You can give crazy huggles and you can even huggle yourself

huggle crazy

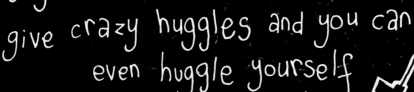

a poem about

Cuddling

I sometimes have feelings
You don't understand
That make me confused and befuddled
So don't go to sleep
When you turn out the light
Cos sometimes I like to be cuddled

us having a lovely cuddle

by
Purple
Ronnie

a poem about a

Huggle

A huggle is something you share
with a friend

You can huggle in all kinds of ways

Huggling makes you feel all sort
of warm

And perfectly splendid for days

us after a good huggle

by Purple Ronnie

a poem to say

I Love You

When I am lying alone in my bed
All sorts of thoughts come into my head
Like why do I Love You as much as I do
Then I know it's because you are You

by
Purple
Ronnie

Getting Married

Getting married is one of the most important things you can ever do. This is what happens:

First the boy asks the girl's Dad if he will let him marry her. This is meant to be a surprise but the girl's Mum has normally found out first

The Dad always says yes — specially if the boy has got lots of money. Then he shakes his hand and tells hundreds of rude stories about him and the Mum

Then the Mum and the girl go shopping for millions of new clothes. They get fancy hairstyles and the girl buys a dress that is much too long for her

Just before the boy gets married his mates go out with him for a feast and they drink masses of beer and try to trick him into DOING IT with other ladies

On the day you get married you have to stand up in front of all the people in the church and the vicar asks you some questions to see how much you Love the other person

Then you must both make some promises of love which go like this

~ LOVE PROMISES ~

① I promise this person that I will look after them forever, specially if they get very poorly.

② I promise this person that I will not have rude thoughts about anyone else and that I will only ever DO IT with them <u>ever</u>.

③ I promise this person that I will share out all my private things like secrets, money and sweets.

④ I promise I won't get cross or giggle if this person whiffs in bed or goes to the lav infront of me because I love all the things about this person (even if they are horrid)

true love   sign↓ here

. . . .

When the girl comes out of church she throws her flowers up in the air and the first person to catch them will be the next to get married

After the marriage everyone goes to a huge party with Love Pie and Cuddle cake and such a saucy drinking potion that they all dance and kiss and happy around until the whole place is bursting full of Love

Right at the end, the marrieds drive off to a secret place with all their presents where they go to bed and get ready to love eachother for the whole of the rest of their life

a poem about Bottoms

Some people's bottoms are skinny and small
And some are all fat and enormous
Some are all hairy and covered in spots
But yours is just totally gorgeous

builder's bottom

sporty bottom

Sumo bottom

gorgeous bottom

botty trophy

Super Bum

by Purple Ronnie

Chapter 4

Bottoms and Swearing

Bottom Burping

Bottom burps are one of the most useful and amazing things you can do

Sometimes they go off completely by mistake and at other times you can load them up in your bottom bit by bit and fire them out at precisely the right moment

Some of the best uses for bottom burps are:

making room in crowded spaces

embarrassing other people

& showing off to friends at Bottom Matches

a poem about ↓

Bottie Coughs

Why do people's Bottie Coughs
Smell of eggs and ham?
I wish they smelt of apple pie
Or scrumptious strawberry jam

eggy
whiff

FFRRP

Poo-ee

JAM 'O' FRESH

by Purple Ronnie

SWEARING

Swearing is great but it can be difficult to do properly unless you have had a lot of practice

Safety

First of all you must learn the rules because swearing can be very dangerous indeed

The Rules of Swearing

1. DO NOT swear at things that are bigger than you

2. NEVER swear in tight spaces

3. ALWAYS have a getaway route planned

4. NEVER swear at friends - even if you're only joking

Choosing Your Words

For the best swears you must choose your words very carefully. You often only get one good chance for each swear so you must not fluff it

Word Groups

Here are some of the best words arranged into groups

Surprise Words		Bottom Words		Noise Words
Crikey	*	Botty	!	Crackle
Heck		Pants		Whiff
Flip	☺	Willy	☆	Fizz
Blimey		Fart		Pop

Pick a word from each group to help make great swears. Practise with small swears first and slowly make them longer. You can even add some of your own words

☆ You **must** use the word "off" if you want to do an angry or rude swear ☆

Here is a Happy swear

Here is an unhappy swear

If you get it right a good swear can feel smashing.
Here are some examples of where it is useful:

Getting Rid of Pests

Showing off to Friends

Frightening Old People

 HAPPY SWEARING

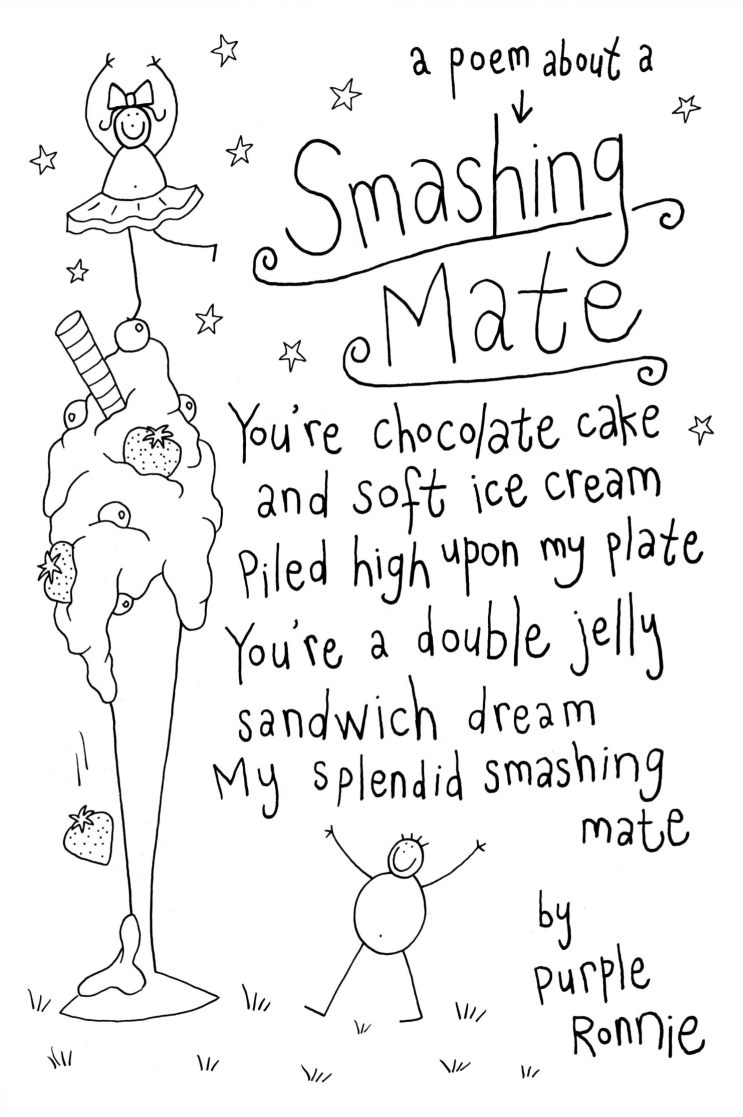

a poem about a

Smashing Mate

You're chocolate cake
and soft ice cream
Piled high upon my plate
You're a double jelly
sandwich dream
My splendid smashing
mate

by
purple
Ronnie

a poem about

Friends

Some people think that it's great to be rich
To be cool and keep up with the trends
But riches and looks just don't matter at all
Cos what really counts is your friends

no cash

Nev's latest tie

Smashing mates

by Purple Ronnie

Friends

One of the things that makes life great is friends

my mates ←

shirlee Gordon me Maisy Nev

Even being very sexy and rich is useless if you haven't got friends

Norman No-mates
I'm so lonesome
speed
vroom
FLASH 1
bounce

Because friends are what make things FUN

If you're feeling sad friends can take away your sadness

And if you're feeling happy friends can double the happiness

Friends can make all sorts of things worth doing that you would never do on your own

And friends can make everyday things feel like you're doing them for the first time

Friends can be nosey and friends can get you into trouble

But REAL FRIENDS are the smashingest things you can have

The History of Private Parts

Ages ago when people first started speaking they found the cleverest man in the world and they gave him the job of thinking up good words and names for everything he could see

Because everyone went around bare the first thing he saw was men's parts. These were easy to think up loads of names for because they behaved in all sorts of funny ways

But when his girlfriend asked him to think up a good name for her parts he suddenly realized that he had used up all his part words and he didn't have any left

He spent ages trying to come up with a good word but he found it very difficult because his girl's parts didn't dangle around like his. In the end he died of brainache

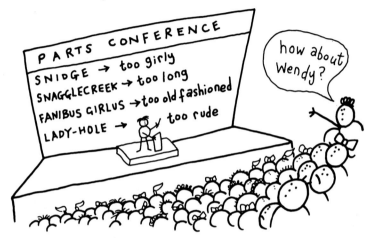

Ever since then the brainiest people from all over the world have tried to think up a good word

But to this day a girl's parts are the one thing left in the whole world that still doesn't have a proper name

a poem about

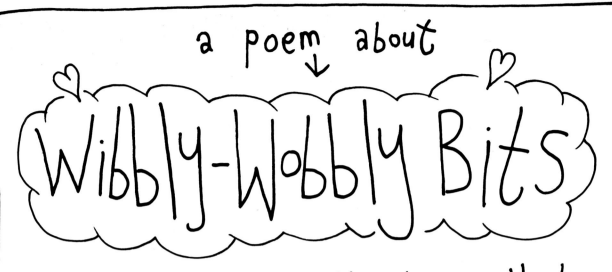

Wibbly-Wobbly Bits

Some people say they're called
bosoms
Others just say they're called tits
But the words I like best
For describing your chest
Are your <u>wibbly</u>-<u>wobbly</u> bits

....mmmm
wibbly-
wobbly
bits

by
Purple
Ronnie

Purple Ronnie's Guide to PANTS

Pant Fact 1

Pants were the first invention ever in the whole world. The first pants were made of leaves and bits of string

try my latest fig pants

EVE'S PANTY PARLOUR

Leaf pants were not very good because:

1 They went brown and mouldy too quickly

yuk!

whiff

2 Everyone could tell when you were doing a bottom burp

flutter

FLURB

Pant Fact 2

In the Olden Days Knights in armour invented spiky metal pants for their girlfriends to wear

Ooooch

they're my best pair

These were abolished when men started wanting to wear girls' undies

Pant Fact 3

Make-you-look-like-you've-got-a-giant-Doodah Pants were invented by Shakespeare

oh gentil squire thy codpiece is most smashingly groovy

These are still worn by Pop Stars and Neville

it's real honestly

bulge →

Pant Styles

Granny Pants

Granny Pants stretch from just under your armpits to just above your feet. They are made from thick baggy sacks and are covered in frills. Granny pants always smell of poison

Sports Pants

Sports pants are for squeezing men's bits into the smallest shape possible. Only to be worn for short periods of time or your privates might melt

French Pants

French pants are for looking sexy in. They are so slippery that if you aren't careful you can slide off your chair and collapse on the floor

Squashing Pants

Squashing pants squish your tummy and bottom together to make you look thinner. When you wear squashing pants steam comes out of your ears, you walk in a funny way and sometimes bits of tummy squish out over the edge

String Pants

No-one knows why string pants were invented. Do not wear them infront of girls. String pants are good for straining homemade beer and catching fish

G-String Pants

G-string pants are like tying a tiny hanky round your parts. Do not wear G-string pants if you have a flabby bottom cos you might not find them again for ages

a poem about

Men's Bits

Men's bits sometimes look like
bananas
And sometimes like shrivelled up
grapes
But however they try
They just can't deny
That they come in the silliest
shapes

titter

I'm not laughing

oo...er what's so funny?

by Purple Ronnie

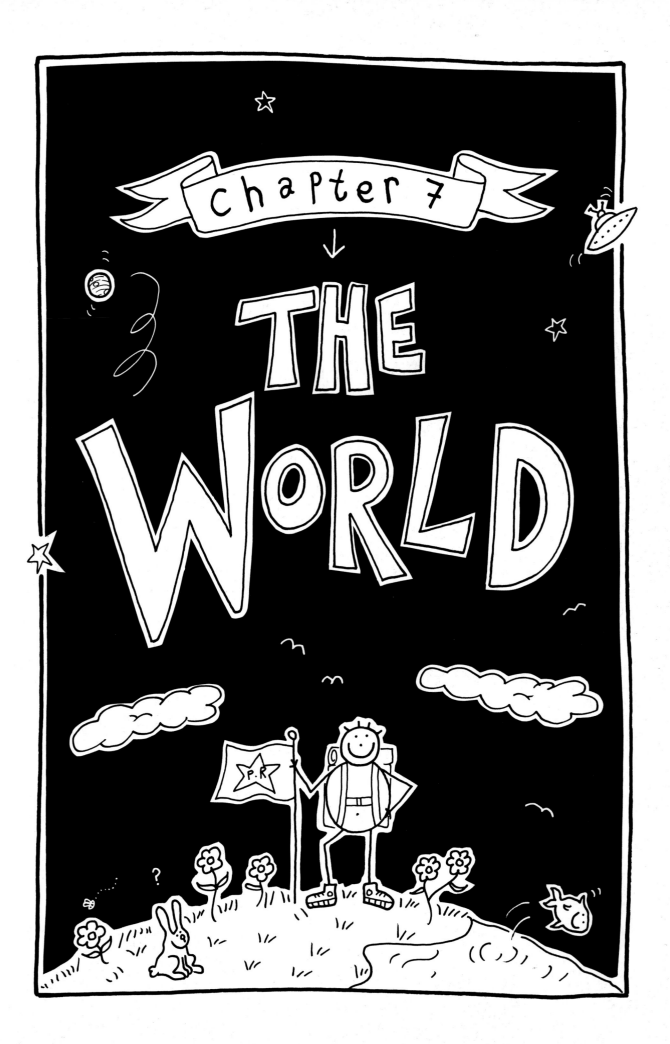

The Beginning of Time

Imagine a place where there were no burgers or beer or hot dogs

Imagine a place without chips or chocolate or chocolate chips or ketchup or anything

Imagine a place where there's nothing to natter about and no-one to cuddle up with

Imagine a place where nothing's ever on T.V. and there's no T.V. not to watch it on

Imagine a place where it's night all the time, where it's cold and dark and lonely

That's what it was like in the beginning of time when the only person around was GOD

Not surprisingly God didn't think it was much fun.
He was bored and lonely and sometimes quite scared

And because it was dark he quite
often bumped into things

When God went to bed he used to shut his eyes
and dream for hours about inventing this place that
he could muck around and have fun in

There would be all sorts of smells and feelings and tastes in this place and every day there would be friends to explore new things with

He wanted something like a gigantic bouncy castle with flowers and trees and monkeys and butterflies and streams and mountains and stuff like that

Then all of a sudden God had a brilliant idea. He saved up loads of his most powerful magic and mixed it up with his biggest wishes then he sprinkled on top his most powerful spell in history EVER

That night God didn't have
any dreams at all and
when he looked out of the
window the next day
he felt smashing

Dangling from the roof
of the sky was a sort of
gigantic round pudding

All the grooviest treats and
surprises he'd ever wanted
were stuffed inside that
pudding. what's more he
was the king of it

yippee!

swing

HO HO HO

For the first time in his
life God laughed...

...He had invented THE WORLD

Names for new invention
· THE PUDDING X
· SUPERLAND ?
· THE WORLD ✓
· NORMAN
  SNACKELFIZZER X
  ↑ too
  muddly

The First People

The first people were Adam and Eve. They lived in the world when it was almost brand new. The trouble is they couldn't find any instructions to go with it

Because of this they quite often got in a muddle about how to work all the new things and what it was like to be people

First of all they went around completely bare

When they felt hungry they didn't know what to eat or how to get it into their tummies

And when they felt saucy they had to try millions of experiments before they got it right

Adam and Eve thought that Doing It was one of the best inventions ever, so they had millions of babies who all found girlfriends or boyfriends and had millions more babies

In the end all the different places in the world became full of people. Most of them were friendly and polite but some of them are still very naughty

Because of this God had to make a list of important instructions which people must <u>never</u> forget

These are the main ones...

INSTRUCTIONS FOR LIVING

1. Thou shalt not have rude thoughts about thy mate's girlfriend

2. Thou art not allowed Ketchup _and_ mustard with thy sausages

3. Thou shalt not leave hairy bits in the bath

4. If thy enemy bashes thee in thou shalt ask him to bog off politely

5. Thou shalt always say thy girlfriend looks fantastic when she dresses up

6. Thou shalt not point at baldies

7. If thou eatest not thy meat thou canst not have any pudding

8. Thou shalt not waft thy bottom burps towards other people and pretend that thou was not the maker of the bottom burp in the first place

9. Thou shalt not try to escape the washing up

10. Thou shalt not squash thy girlfriend out of the bed, nor shalt thou hog the blankets

What Happens in Hell

They gather all the bottom burps
You've done when you're alive
And tried to blame on someone else
instead

Then wait until you're just about
to snog a saucy girl
And empty the whole sackload on your
head

They wire up your privates
Then they dip you in ice cream
And ask a hundred girls to have a scoff
But if you move a muscle
Or your doodah starts to grow
The wires touch and blow your goolies off

They've got a giant movie screen
On which they show your life
And blare out all the secrets that
you have

Then they pause and show slow motions
of the stupid things you've done
With action replays of you on the lav

Toilets in Hell

Eating in Hell

Friends in Hell

The End of the World

I hope that I'm there at the End of the World
When everyone stands in a queue
And says all the wickedest things that they've done
And the bad things they've wanted to do

Naughty folk's heads will cave in and explode
And goo will spurt out of their brains
Their tummies will tangle and turn inside out
And their bottoms will burst into flames

But people like me who've been lovely and kind
Will rocket straight up to the sky
And watch the whole rumpus from big squashy beds
With loads of free ale and fudge pie

And angels will cuddle and stroke us
And say how fantastic we are
And how out of all of the people they've met
We're the smashingly coolest by far

How to DO iT

Foreplay

First of all you must give the girl masses of beer and sweets and tell her lots of brilliant jokes

After this she will think you are amazing and you must stick your tongue out and lick her ear about ten times but you must not chew or munch it

Then you must tickle the girl and if she wriggles then it means she is ready to be TURNED ON

Gadgets

It is always best to use protection but you must make sure you get the right sort

wrong

Sometimes you can use special love gadgets and put on saucy pants

buzz

← our amazing love gadgets

Actually Doing IT

It is polite to ask the girl first if you can DO IT with her and if she says 'yes please' you must close your eyes while she takes off her clothes and stuff.

...um can I do IT with you?

yes please

Then you must snuggle up very close together and wriggle and snog and squeal all at the same time. DO NOT laugh at the girl's bosoms or wobble them around because bosoms are not funny-they are AMAZING

wriggle

squeal!

snog

snuggle

Knobs and Switches

Girls have knobs under their jersies that you have to twist and a special switch to turn on the electricity in their pants

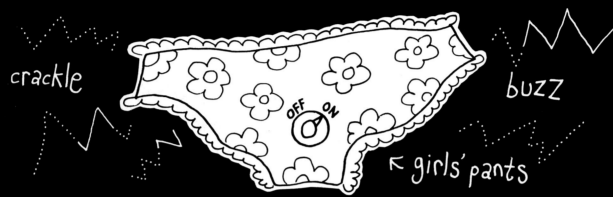

crackle

buzz

OFF ON

← girls' pants

If you forget about these you might as well go home because girls have to be <u>turned on</u> properly to DO IT

The G-Spot

The G-Spot was discovered ten years ago by an incredibly brainy scientist. It is very small and can only be seen with a special microscope. If you find it you must not press too hard or it might explode and make a terrible mess

Professor Rude →

Oooohh aaahh

After Doing IT

You must not stop DOING IT until the girl says you can, then you must hug the girl and tell her she is smashing for ages. DO NOT punch the girl if she snores

Things not to say after DOING IT
1. Thanks
2. Do you want some money?
3. Can I go to the toilet now?

Love

If you want to snuggle, squeal, snog and hug with the girl all the time then you are probably feeling LOVE. Do not worry about this because LOVE is the most AMAZING THING THAT HAS EVER BEEN INVENTED

a poem about ↓

Sex Maniacs

They dream about sex every hour of the
day
They dream when they work
And they dream when they play
They dream about sex in the bath
and in bed
They never get naughty thoughts out of
their head

by Purple Ronnie

a poem about

Safe Sex

To make sure you're safe when you DO IT
Put on a Thingie that fits
I like the ones that glow in the dark
With the slippery nobbly bits

rip
tug

are you sure you've done this before?

hundreds of thingies

by Purple Ronnie

a poem about

My Lover

bestest friends

I'd like to tell you something
I hope it won't offend
But if you weren't my lover
You'd be my bestest friend

us wearing
saucy
undies

by
Purple
Ronnie

what is a Grown-up?

Grown-ups can be young or old or anywhere in the middle. What makes you a Grown-up is not how long you have been alive but how **IMPORTANT** and **SERIOUS** your brain feels. Here is a guide on how to spot them:

Grown-ups listen to music that doesn't have any words

Grown-ups learn long words so that people will think they are very important

Grown-ups are useless at making up games so they just stand around and say things

Grown-ups think business and newspapers are the most interesting things in the world

Grown-Upping

There comes a time when grown-ups have done so much businessing and grown-upping around that their muscles go all flabby and their bodies start spreading out all over the place

They get frightened that people will not fancy them anymore so they try to make themselves look sexy by:

showing off their hair →

running around in tight clothes ←

and showing off how much money they've got →

titchy pea

some of them try to stop eating grub which makes them very grumpy

←

and the rich ones just attach themselves to machines →

buzz suck tan

wobble

But being wobbled by machines is boring and not eating is the craziest thing in the world. Who cares about looking sexy when there's so much scrumptious grub and beer

a poem about
Pigging Out

I could take myself out for a jog every day
To lose a few pounds off my bum
Or work out for hours until I'm half dead
But I'd rather pig out and have fun

by Purple Ronnie

munch

Jammy Bun

POP

gobble

twang

crea

us having a good squeeze

a poem about a

Big Belly

I like it when people have
bellies
That are lovely and cuddly
to squeeze
But not great big wobbly jellies
That dangle right down to their
knees

Jelly man

wobble

wobble

by Purple
Ronnie

a poem about a ↓

Squidgey Bum

Some people will do anything
To have a skinny tum
But what I like
Is a smiley face
And a nice fat squidgey <u>Bum</u>

lovely smile ↓

happy ←

squidgey bum →

starve

rumble

by Purple Ronnie

Old People

Old people are what you get when the most grown-up grown-ups stop trying to pretend they're young anymore. This means they can be as utterly barmy and loopy-headed as they like and everyone thinks they're incredible

The main thing old people do is gang together in clubs and go on thousands of outings

Old People Clubs

The Always Being in the Post Office Club

The Saturday morning Club for selling cakes to all your friends

HEAVEN

When old people have had enough of living their Life flies out of them and whizzes up to Heaven

You can only get into Heaven if you have been good so there is quite a difficult test you have to do before you can go in

If you pass the test someone at the door gives you a ticket and it's just like a big Party where everyone floats around hugging and kissing and saying nice things to eachother

hey I really dig your hairstyle